You are th... ... ...
On a day when flowers
aren't enough,
I'll give you my heart.

xo

We all need a little help
hearing the music
sometimes.

All it takes is one note. One toe, tapping.
One heart...

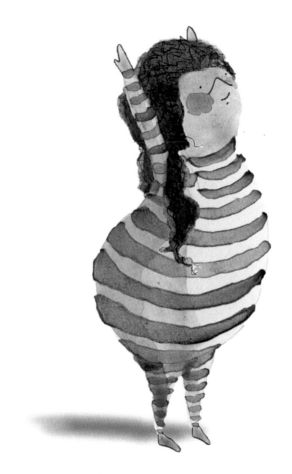

...that begins to dance.

Follow your heart and see where it leads.

That's enough. Really.

Getting to know yourself is half the
battle. The other half is being okay
with who you are.

You're the only one who can change the way you see yourself. For better or for worse. Be kind with you.

If you keep moving your feet, you run the risk
of your dreams coming true.

Eventually, someone will see what once only your heart knew was there.

As good as it feels to have someone believe in you,

it feels even better to believe in yourself.

Confidence is a quiet thing that happens slowly
over time as you're stretching.

Sometimes it happens so slowly you don't even realize
you're standing taller.

There's no one in this world more
perfect to live your dream than you.

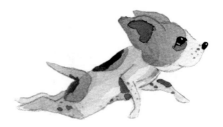

It's good to be clear about who you are. Even if that means some days only knowing who you're not.

It takes time and turning things over to see what was always there.

You
are
only
as
free
as
your
heart
is
open.

For this one glorious and unrehearsed moment, maybe you can trust you're exactly where you need to be.

No matter how old or how young you are, you're always becoming.

The choice is yours.

Someone who's decidedly joyful. Someone who wastes not a minute of their heart. Someone who—whether on one leg or two—dances like their life matters. Because it does.

You're infinitely more exquisite than your thoughts let on.

If each of us takes care of the calling in our heart, if we reach for our dreams and become everything we were made to be, collectively we'll change the world. And wouldn't that be great?

Keep looking for the good. You'll find it. You might even discover it was looking for you too.

Now off you go. Your dreams are waiting. But remember...

Be the one dancing.

And always choose joy.

Author's Note:

In the humblest, most unassuming way, the girls
(and the chicken) in this book know how
wonderful they are. What they don't know is that
wonderful's just the beginning.

How we see ourselves is not a thinking thing. It's
a running and jumping and leaping thing. Or
when we're tired and not feeling well, it's a sitting
quietly, hearts-open thing. As the girls in this
book will attest, we're infinitely more exquisite
than our thoughts let on.

Let joy lead so the world may know—by the way
we carry ourselves—big dreams are alive and well.

P. Marin

P.S. Did you know every book you purchase and share by
P. Marin adds joy to this world? You're making a difference.

To Marco and to Marin.
The two who make my heart sing.
Out loud. Off key. With complete
abandon and joy.
PM

The Goal is Joy

Prints Marin, Ink, Huntington Beach, CA

P. Marin

The Goal is Joy

ISBN-10: 0-9986119-4-8 ISBN-13: 978-0-9986119-4-5

PRINTS MARIN, INK
Find What You Love and Do It Often.
printsmarin.com

Made in United States
North Haven, CT
16 March 2023